The Shadow

Michael Wm. Kaluta
Joel Goss
James Sinclair

BOXTREE

THE SHADOW

Before James Bond, before Indiana Jones, before even Batman, there was the Shadow. Most fans think that this archetypal superhero first turned up in a radio show in the 1930s or 40s. Not true. He appeared first in 1931 as the star of *The Living Shadow*, a pulp novel aimed at listeners of the *Detective Story Half Hour*. Soon the Shadow novels were appearing at the rate of one a month (in all, 325 were published). The radio series came out of the novels and by 1937, with its narration being done by movie legend Orson Wells, the series had become an American institution.

A comic strip, four feature films and several matinee serials followed, not to mention a series of comics, but it was to the original, *noir* novels that screenwriter David Koepp turned when he started researching the character of Lamont Cranston for the Universal Pictures film.

In the first of the pulp novels, Walter B Gibson's creation was little more than a glorified detective, moving furtively through the dark streets of 30s America. It wasn't until the start of the radio series that the magic powers and mysticism began to evolve. In fact, originally the Shadow wasn't even called Lamont Cranston. He was Kent Allard – master spy – and Lamont Cranston was merely one of Allard's identities. But by the time the radio soaps were on air, the Shadow *was* millionaire playboy Lamont Cranston and his real identity as Kent Allard had been forgotten.

There is, however, one extra dimension to the Shadow's new character, a psychic shift appropriate to the times in which we live. The original Shadow, the Shadow of the books and radio plays *appeared* sinister but was actually firmly on the side of truth, justice and the American way. The new Shadow really *is* sinister.

In keeping with the spirit of the 90s, Lamont Cranston's fight against evil is now a fight against himself.

An adaptation from the Universal Pictures film by Micheal Wm. Kaluta – *writer, illustrator, cover artist*; Joel Goss – *writer*; James Sinclair – *colourist*; John Workman – *letterer*; Scott Fuentes – *designer*; Robert Boyd – *editor*.

AND YOU SAY THIS STORY IS TRUE?
SO WHY TELL ME?
BECAUSE IT'S UNBELIEVABLE-- MY PAPER WON'T PRINT IT. BUT YOU WORK FOR THE CLASSIC, BURKE, AND THEY'LL PRINT ANYTHING.
BESIDES, I'M A FINANCIAL WRITER FOR THE TIMES, NOT ON THE CRIME BEAT.
AND I AM. ALL RIGHT-- WHY DON'T YOU TELL ME WHAT YOU THINK YOU'VE FIGURED OUT.
OKAY, THIS SHOULD DO IT...
NOW, REMEMBER, I'VE PIECED THIS TOGETHER AS BEST I COULD-- AND OF COURSE, I'VE HAD TO FILL IN SOME GAPS WITH... SPECULATION. BUT I FOUND SOME EYEWITNESSES WHERE IT STARTED, HERE IN NEW YORK...

OPEN THE HOOD, E.J.-- IF ANYBODY SPOTS US, THEY'LL THINK IT'S ENGINE TROUBLE.
DRAG HIM OUT, MAXIE.
I DIDN'T SEE ANY-THING, I PROMISE!
SHUT UP, WOIM!
I WON'T TALK, I'M TELLING YOU!
I KNOW YOU WON'T.
GIVE HIM THE WORKS.
WHAT THE HELL--?
WHO'S THERE?
I WARNED YOU ONCE BEFORE, DUKE ROLLINS. THE WEED OF CRIME BEARS BITTER FRUIT.
THIS AIN'T GOOD. LET'S SCRAM!
JUST 'CAUSE YOU GOT THE DROP ON ME ONCE DON'T MEAN YOU CAN DO IT AGAIN. NOBODY MAKES A MONKEY OUTTA ME TWICE!
SLAM!
BLAM!
BLAMM!

YOU GET HIM, DUKE?
YOU'RE DAMN RIGHT I--
CRUNK

YOU COMMITTED MURDER THIS TIME, DUKE, AND YOU'RE GOING TO PAY FOR IT.

YOU WILL PAY, DUKE.

LIKE HELL--

BRATATATATATATTAT
YOU HAVE TWO ALTERNATIVES-- SURRENDER TO THE POLICE...

...OR FACE MY WRATH.

I'M GETTIN' OUTTA HERE.

DON'T TAKE DUKE'S CAR HE'LL NEED IT HE CHOOSES DISREGARD ME.

THE *HELL* YOU SAY...
GO! GO! GO!

WHAT THE HELL?

IT IS YOUR CHOICE, DUKE ROLLINS. THE LAW OR ME.

AND NOW FOR YOU...
PLEASE--

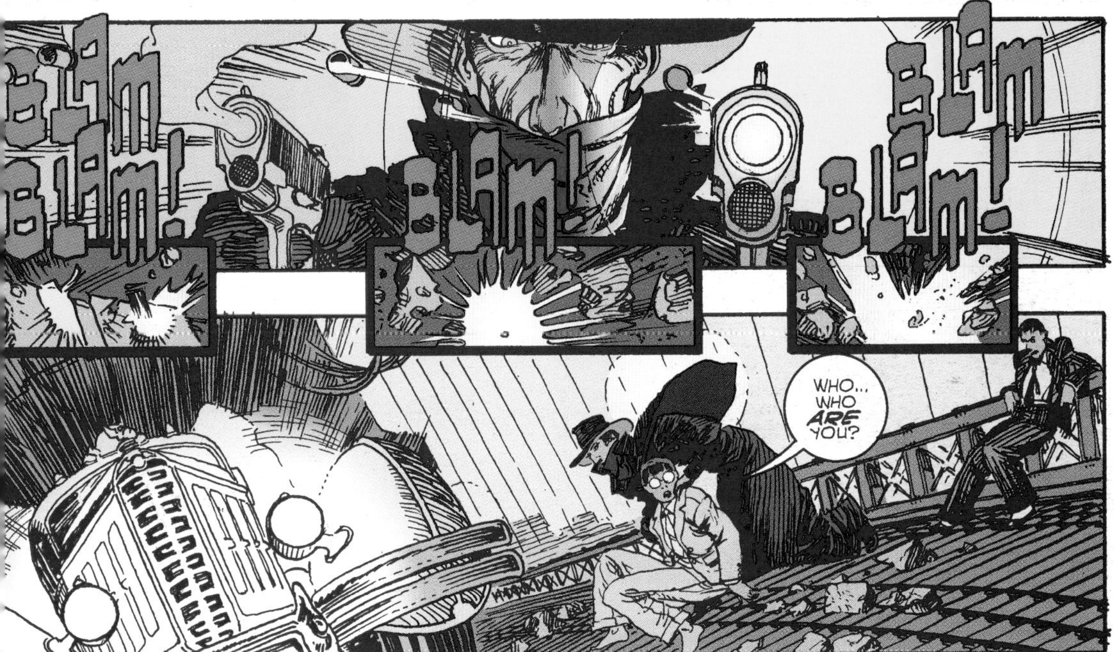
BLAM BLAM!
BLAM!
BLAM BLAM!
WHO... WHO ARE YOU?

I'LL SEE YOU SOON, DUKE... IN JAIL OR IN HELL.

DRIVE.

THAT'S ONE TOUGH BUNCH-- I'VE SEEN THEM AROUND THE NEIGHBORHOOD BEFORE.
I KNOW.
I ALSO KNOW WHO YOU ARE, DOCTOR ROY TAM, A PROFESSOR OF SCIENCE.
WHY, YES.
I'VE SAVED YOUR LIFE, ROY TAM.
YEAH. GREAT. YOU'VE JUST POSTPONED THE INEVITABLE. I'M IN DUTCH NOW-- MY LIFE ISN'T WORTH A PLUGGED NICKEL. THE REST OF THIS GANG IS GOING TO BLAME ME FOR WHAT JUST HAPPENED.
I WILL PROTECT YOU.
THE DRIVER... MISTER SHREVNITZ... WILL INSTRUCT YOU IN THE WAY I WILL CONTACT YOU, SHOULD I REQUIRE YOUR HELP.
HOW DID YOU FIGURE WHO I AM AND WHAT WAS HAPPENING TO ME?
HAHAHAHA!
THE SHADOW KNOWS.
HAHAHAHA!
HERE YOU ARE...
...SAFE AND SOUND.
DON'T EVER TAKE IT OFF.
BE SEEING YOU.

BOSS... YOU OKAY?
THE COBALT CLUB, SHREVVY-- I MUST... MEET SOMEONE.
YOU'RE LATE AGAIN, LAMONT.
SORRY, COMMISSIONER. THERE WAS A LITTLE --ACCIDENT ON THE BRIDGE.
I GOT CAUGHT UP.
YOU GOT CAUGHT UP.
LAMONT?

FRANKLY, LAMONT, I SOMETIMES WONDER WHY YOU KEEP CALLING ME FOR DINNER.
URGENT MESSAGE FOR YOU, POLICE COMMISSIONER.

WHAT'S THE MATTER?

I HAVE TO LEAVE. IT'S THIS--THIS SHADOW SITUATION AGAIN.
I THOUGHT THAT WAS JUST A RUMOR.

NOT ACCORDING TO DUKE ROLLINS. AN ANONYMOUS TIP SAID WE'D FIND THIS GANGSTER ROLLINS ON THE BROOKLYN BRIDGE.

HE CONFESSED TO MURDER, BABBLING ABOUT PROTECTION FROM THE SHADOW. TOOK THREE STRONG OFFICERS TO PRY HIM OFF THE EDGE.

TOMORROW I'M GOING TO APPOINT ANOTHER TASK FORCE TO INVESTIGATE.

YOU'RE NOT GOING TO APPOINT A TASK FORCE. THE LAST ONE CONCLUDED THERE WAS NOTHING TO INVESTIGATE.
AH, THE HELL WITH ANOTHER TASK FORCE.
SORRY-- WHERE WAS I?
YOU WERE GOING TO TELL ME WHO SHE IS BEFORE YOU LEFT.
OH... MISS MARGO LANE.

WONDER IF I COULD HAVE A GLASS OF MOUTON--
--ROTHSCHILD, 1928.

WHY, YES.
LAMONT CRANSTON. MIND IF I SIT?

IT'S THE STRANGEST THING. I HAVE A SUDDEN CRAVING FOR PEKING DUCK.
THAT'S ODD. I WAS JUST THINKING THE SAME THING.
SERENDIPITY. SHALL WE ORDER?

AMERICAN MUSEUM OF NATURAL HISTORY...
WELL? WHAT IS IT?
I DON'T KNOW, MISTER NEWBOLDT. I'D HAVE LABELED IT A MUMMY CASE, EXCEPT IT CAME FROM TIBET--
MY GOD, IT'S BEAUTIFUL. HELP ME GET THE SIDES OFF!
"THE KHA KHAN. THE POWER OF GOD ON EARTH."
THIS IS THE SILVER COFFIN OF GENGHIS KHAN.
I MUST MAKE A PHONE CALL.
CLEAN UP THIS MESS, BERGER, BUT DON'T TOUCH THAT COFFIN!
NO, SIR.

NO SIR-REE!
SNAP!
SNAP!
SNAP!
SNAP!
SACRIFICE YOURSELF TO ME...
FALL TO YOUR KNEES...
SACRIFICE YOURSELF TO ME.
YES...
...MY...
...KHAN.
BERGER?
BERG--

JOIN ME OR DIE...

WELL, THANK YOU, MISTER CRANSTON--
I HAD A WONDERFUL TIME. I'M SORRY, BUT I PROMISED MY FATHER I'D VISIT HIM TONIGHT.
I CAN'T RECALL AN EVENING AS... STIMULATING.

YOU'RE A VERY UNUSUAL MAN, MISTER CRANSTON.
YOU KNEW THE WINE I WANTED AND SHARED MY CRAVING FOR PEKING DUCK--YOU SEEM TO KNOW WHAT I WANT AT THE SAME TIME I DO.

I BELIEVE YOU WERE TRYING TO SEDUCE ME.
CALL IT A SIXTH SENSE.

WELL, GOOD NIGHT, MISTER CRANSTON.

GOOD NIGHT, MISS MARGO LANE...

AH. AT LAST.

DID YOU HEAR ME, REINHARDT?
I'M FINISHED WITH MY SPHERE.
THE IDEA YOU HAD OF FORMING A CONTROLLED METAL BUBBLE IN THE WATER TANK WORKED BEAUTIFULLY.
GOOD. GREAT.
SO I'D LIKE TO GET THE ARMY BRASS IN TO REVIEW...
I'VE TOLD YOU A DOZEN TIMES... WE'RE DOING ENERGY RESEARCH. I'M NOT INTERESTED IN ANY MILITARY APPLICATIONS.
WAR DEPARTMENT
AUTHORIZED PERSONNEL ONLY

SO WHY LET THE WAR DEPARTMENT PAY THE BILLS?
I NEED MONEY TO FINISH MY EXPERIMENTS. THEY HAVE IT.

YOU DON'T THINK BIG, LANE. IF YOU'D LISTEN TO ME, THE WORLD COULD BE OUR OYSTER.

I GET A RASH FROM OYSTERS!

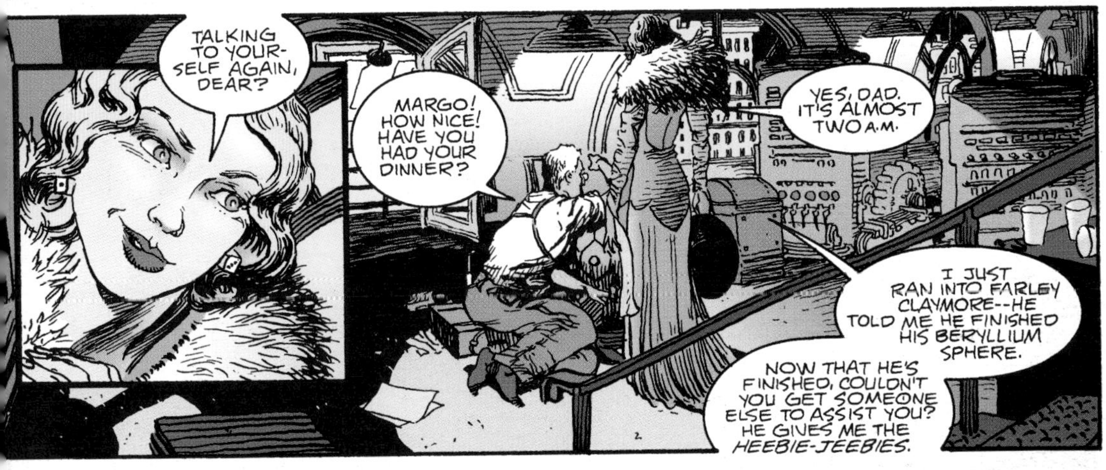
TALKING TO YOURSELF AGAIN, DEAR?
MARGO! HOW NICE! HAVE YOU HAD YOUR DINNER?
YES, DAD. IT'S ALMOST TWO A.M.
I JUST RAN INTO FARLEY CLAYMORE--HE TOLD ME HE FINISHED HIS BERYLLIUM SPHERE.
NOW THAT HE'S FINISHED, COULDN'T YOU GET SOMEONE ELSE TO ASSIST YOU? HE GIVES ME THE *HEEBIE-JEEBIES*.

DAD?

SHOUP!
PHFFTT!
B. JONAS

CHUNK!

B. Jonas

REPORT.

AGENT REPORTS TWO MURDERS AT AMERICAN MUSEUM OF NATURAL HISTORY--ADVISES INQUIRY. SENT POSSIBLE EVIDENCE FROM CRIME SCENE.
PFFT
CLUNK

KHAN.

SHIWAN KHAN. AND YOU ARE THE SHADOW OF YOUR FORMER SELF--LAMONT CRANSTON.
IN TIBET, WE KNEW YOU BY A DIFFERENT NAME--YING KO.
I HAVE USED MANY NAMES.

I TRAVELED TO THIS COUNTRY IN GENGHIS KHAN'S HOLY CRYPT TO FULLY ABSORB HIS POWER.
I HAVE COME TO PAINT MY MASTER STROKE.
IN THREE DAYS, ON THE ANNIVERSARY OF HIS BIRTH-- THE YEAR OF THE SWINE-- THE ENTIRE WORLD WILL HEAR MY ROAR AND WILLINGLY FALL SUBJECT TO THE LOST EMPIRE OF SIANKING.
ASTER TULKU SPOKE YOU CONSTANTLY. WASN'T ABLE TO RN ME QUITE AS EASILY.
THIS I TOOK FROM MASTER TULKU WHEN I LEFT, AFTER I RAN IT THROUGH HIS HEART.
OPPORTUNITIES FOR ADVANCEMENT ARE LIMITED IN TIBET.
YOU MIGHT SAY I FOLLOWED IN YOUR FOOTSTEPS TO A CERTAIN DEGREE.
IS THAT WHAT HAPPENED? OR DID I LEAD YOU--TO A CERTAIN DEGREE?
AMUSING NOTION.
JOIN ME, YING KO. TOGETHER, WE'LL PIT ARMIES AGAINST ARMIES, COLLECT OUR DUE OF PAIN, WASH OUR HANDS IN BLOOD.
YOUR MOUTH STILL WATERS AT REAL POWER. I'M OFFERING YOU A LAST CHANCE TO TAKE IT BACK. BE MY PARTNER, YING KO.
EEP THE COIN, FOR YOUR TIME.
CONSIDER MY PROPOSAL.
WE'LL MEET AGAIN.

I'M SORRY, MISTER CRANSTON... THE METAL HAS DEFIED ALL OUR ANALYSIS...
PLEASE CONSIDER DEEPLY, DOCTOR TAM...

...THE COIN IS, AFTER ALL, CHINESE.

WELL, THERE IS ONE LAST POSSIBILITY. VERY REMOTE, BUT WE MAY AS WELL BE CERTAIN.

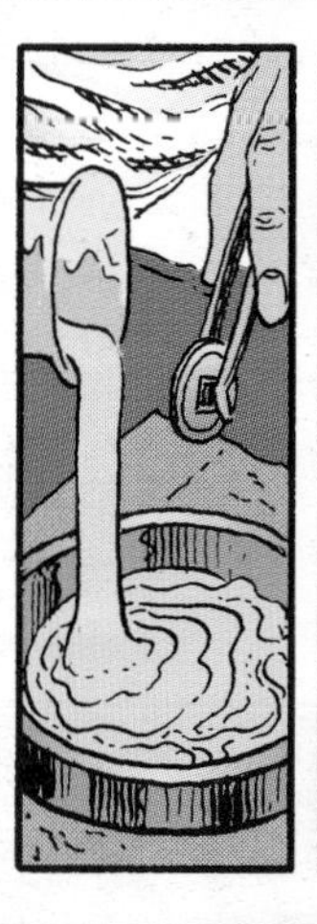

BRONZIUM!

THE ANCIENT CHINESE BELIEVED THIS WAS THE VERY STUFF OF WHICH THE UNIVERSE WAS FORMED.

WHAT COULD THIS BRONZIUM BE USED FOR?
WELL--IT'S SUPPOSED TO BE VERY UNSTABLE ON THE MOLECULAR LEVEL, CONSTANTLY GIVEN TO EXPANSION. ONLY THE CELL BONDS HOLD IT IN CHECK. BUT IF THOSE WERE EVER BREACHED--
BY EXPLOSION?

WOULDN'T DO IT. APPARENTLY THE WHOLE PURPOSE OF THE CELL DESIGN IS TO RESIST THAT KIND OF FORCE--BUT BY IMPLOSION, THE MOLECULAR IMBALANCE WOULD BE INTENSIFIED AND ULTIMATELY RELEASED.
AND?

THE RELEASE OF THAT ENERGY COULD TRIGGER A LARGER, CATASTROPHIC REACTION--AN IMPLOSIVE/ EXPLOSIVE SUB-MOLEC- ULAR WEAPON.
A BOMB ?

INDEED! BUT YOU'D NEED A SHELL... A SPHERE THAT WOULD CONTAIN THE APPARATUS AND FOCUS THE RELEASED ENERGY.
WHAT WOULD IT TAKE TO DESIGN THE IMPLOSIVE DEVICE?

LOOK INTO MY GIRASOL. SPECULATE BEYOND WHAT YOU CONSIDER POSSIBLE.
WELL, THE DEVICE SHOULD HAVE TINY, POWERFUL IMPLOSIVE CHARGES REGULARLY SPACED OVER ITS SURFACE...
...PERHAPS SOMETHING LIKE THIS.
IT WOULD HAVE TO BE ENCASED IN A REFLECTIVE SHELL. BERYLLIUM WOULD PROBABLY BE THE BEST; IT WOULD ENHANCE THE BLAST.
"OF COURSE, THIS IS PURE CONJECTURE..."
REINHARDT LANE.
REINHARDT LANE.
REINHARDT LANE.

REINHARDT LANE
DAD, COME AWAY FROM THE...

YOU WILL BRING YOUR EXPERIMENT TO ME.
YES, MY KHAN. BUT HOW? THE SECURITY...
TELL ME OF THIS SECURITY. WHEN IT IS WEAKEST, I WILL SEE TO IT THAT YOU HAVE... ASSISTANCE.
YES, MY KHAN.
GO TO BED, DAD.
OH, DAMN. IT'S THAT MISS LANE AGAIN. SHE'S BEEN CALLING ME SINCE EARLY THIS MORNING...
MISS LANE! DELIGHTFUL TO--
IT'S ABOUT MY FATHER.
EVER SINCE LAST NIGHT, HE'S BEEN WALKING AROUND IN A DAZE, TALKING TO HIMSELF...
...AND TONIGHT.
MISS LANE, THE FACT THAT YOU SAY YOUR FATHER IS ACTING STRANGELY DOES NOT JUSTIFY POLICE INVESTIGATION.

PERHAPS IT'S HIS WORK... TOP SECRET? IT IS THE WAR DEPARTMENT, AND--
NO, HIS PROJECT IS HARMLESS IMPLOSION ENERGY RESEARCH.

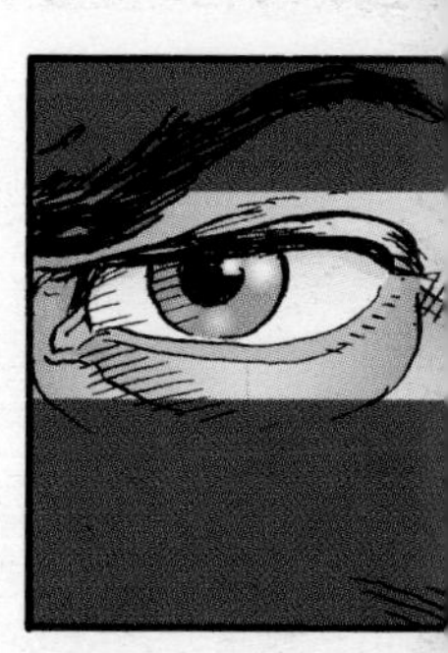

SOMETHING'S VERY WRONG. I KNOW IT.
ALL RIGHT. I'LL SEND A SQUAD CAR 'ROUND THE FEDERAL BUILDING IF IT'LL MAKE YOU FEEL BETTER.
LAMONT, WHY DON'T YOU GO--
LAMONT?

FEDERAL
DING...
HOW ABOUT A COUPLE HAMBURGER SANDWICHES?
HORIZE
I FEEL LIKE INDIAN--
ZZZZZIK!

URKGG!

ZZZZZZZIK!

PLINK

UMFF!

ssip
sssipp
sssipp
BLAM!
BLAM!

TZZZING!

BLAM!
BLAM!

I DIE FOR MY KHAN.

ALL OF THEM?!
YES, MY KHAN.
IT IS YING KO. IT HAS TO BE.
BEGIN YOUR WORK, INCORPORATING THIS BRONZIUM INTO YOUR DESIGN. YOU WILL NOT DOUBT YOUR WORK--
--YOU WILL GO BEYOND THE LIMITS YOU SET UPON YOURSELF AND DO YOUR BEST WITH NO RESTRICTIONS IN YOUR OWN MIND.
YES, MY KHAN.
OHHUH...
WHAT IS ALL THIS? WHAT ARE YOU DOING WITH MY FATHER?
HE IS COMPLETELY IN MY POWER-- AS YOU SOON SHALL BE.
LISTEN TO MY VOICE, MARGO LANE...

I HEAR IT. BUT I DON'T HEAR ANY EXPLANATIONS...

AH, ONE OF THE STRONG ONES.
I'M SORRY I DON'T HAVE MORE TIME TO BEND YOU TO MY WILL.

NOW... I HAVE A MISSION FOR YOU, MY DEAR.

SO SHIWAN KHAN TRAVELS TO THIS COUNTRY IN THE SOLID SILVER SARCOPHAGUS OF HIS ANCESTOR GENGHIS KHAN, ABSORBING ITS ANCIENT POWER...
"HE'S GOT A TOP SCIENTIST, REINHARDT LANE, UNDER HIS THUMB AND PLANS TO TAKE OVER THE WORLD, STARTING WITH THE DESTRUCTION OF NEW YORK."
"WELL? GET ON WITH IT."
"REMEMBER, NOW--ALL OF THIS IS TRUE, I SWEAR. I HAVE PAPERS TO PROVE MOST OF IT.
"SHIWAN KHAN NARCOTIZED MARGO LANE, GAVE HER A PISTOL...
"... AND SENT HER OUT TO FIND THE SHADOW."

THE SHADOW, IN HIS GUISE AS LAMONT CRANSTON, WAS AT THE SITE OF THE OLD HOTEL MONOLITH, WHERE HE HAD EARLIER LOST KHAN'S TRAIL.
20¢ 1/4
5¢ EA.
KLIK
KABLAM

HOTEL MONOLITH
1928
MARGO!

OHH...

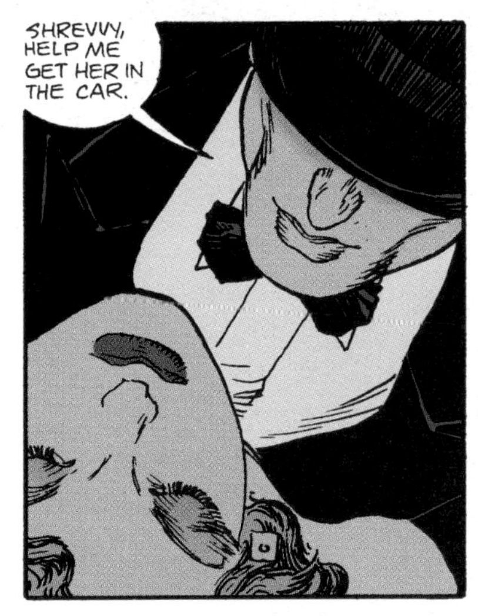
SHREVVY, HELP ME GET HER IN THE CAR.

THERE WAS THIS VOICE...
THIS KID IS COKED TO THE EYE-BALLS...

...IT TOLD ME TO SHOOT THE SHADOW...

...AND IT SENT ME TO YOU!

YOU'RE-- THE SHADOW.

MARGO, KHAN WANTED ME TO KILL YOU, ELSE HE WOULD HAVE SENT HIS TRAINED ASSASSINS.
KHAN NOW HAS YOUR FATHER AND HIS IMPLOSION DEVICE. HE MUST ALSO HAVE A BERYLLIUM SPHERE TO BE USED AS A DETONATING SHELL, OR THE BOMB IS NEAR HARMLESS.
DAD'S ASSISTANT... CLAYMORE... WAS WORKING ON A BERYLLIUM SPHERE. HE'D BRAGGED ABOUT COMPLETING IT.
AT YOUR FATHER'S LAB IN THE FEDERAL BUILDING?
NO... DOWNTOWN AT MARITECH LAB...
TELL ME ALL, MARGO... AND THEN SLEEP...
A SHORT TIME LATER...
WAIT DOWN THE BLOCK, SHREVVY. FOLLOW ANYONE WHO LEAVES...
MARIT
IT'S AS I TOLD YOU...
WITHOUT THE REFLECTIVE FORCE OF THE BERYLLIUM SPHERE, THE DETONATION WILL BE NO MORE THAN A MORERATE TO HEAVY AERIAL BOMB--

BUT WITH THE EXPLOSION CONTAINED WITHIN THE SPHERE...
...FORCING THE RADIATION BACK IN ON ITSELF...
...WE CAN SEE THE DESTRUCTIVE POWER OF A HUNDREDTH PART OF THE SUN!
HEE HEE HEE.
RATATTRAT
BLAMM!
HEE HEE HEE.
SLAM!

ARE YOU STILL ALIVE IN THERE?
FARLEY CLAYMORE--YOUR MIND IS BEING MANIPULATED BY UNSPEAKABLE EVIL!
MANIPULATED?
HEE, HEE--YOU'RE THE ONE BEING MANIPULATED!
I GLADLY WORK FOR MY KHAN!
THERE'S A NEW WORLD COMING AND I'M GOING TO BE A KING.
A KING!
KHAN TOLD ME YOU WERE AN ARROGANT FOOL... AND NOW IT'S GONNA COST YOU!
GURGLE
I'LL BE GONE FOR A WHILE...
FWOOSH!
DON'T HOLD YOUR BREATH!
DON'T HOLD YOUR BREATH, HEE HEE.
SSSSSSS

MARI TEC
LAB
HERE WE GO... THE BOSS HAS FLUSHED OUT ONE OF THE RATS...
25¢
MILE

MANIPULATED... HEE HEE HEE...

MARGO...
I NEED YOU...
SHREVVY, WE'VE GOT TO GO BACK.
STOP THE CAR!
NO DICE... I GOT A JOB TO DO.
STOP THE CAR OR I'LL BLOW YOUR BRAINS ALL OVER THE DASHBOARD.

JEEZO! SUIT YERSELF!
SHREEEEEECHH!

I'M COMING, LAMONT...
SCRAPE!

BWOOSH!
MARGO...
LAMONT, I...
QUIET, NOW. EVER THING'S OKAY.

BOSS!
I TRACKED 'IM, BOSS, AND YOU'LL NEVER GUESS...
HOLY HANNA!
AGAIN?

H ATOP KHAN'S REFUGE:
FROM ABOUT THERE... TO **THERE.**
THAT WILL BE THE RANGE OF DESTRUCTION?

THAT'S JUST EXPLOSION ELF... THE STRUCTION WILL BE ALCULABLE.

HERE ARE THE BLUEPRINTS, MY KHAN.
THANK YOU, FARLEY.

THESE COPIES MAKE PROFESSOR LANE OBSOLETE.
OBSOLETE. YES. YESS.

SET THE TIMER, REINHARDT, THEN GO WITH MY MEN.
LEAVE HIM IN A ROOM WITH THE BOMB. HE WILL DIE BY HIS OWN INVENTION.

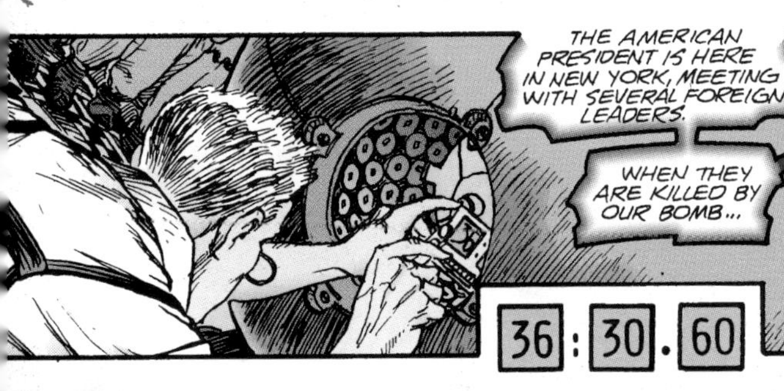

THE AMERICAN PRESIDENT IS HERE IN NEW YORK, MEETING WITH SEVERAL FOREIGN LEADERS.
WHEN THEY ARE KILLED BY OUR BOMB...
36 : 30 . 60

I WILL PPEAR FROM E CHAOS AND CK UP THE REINS OF POWER.
VICTORY IS OURS!

AND AS VICTORS, WE SHALL COLLECT THE SPOILS OF WAR!

YOU WILL ALL BE REMEMBERED-- ESPECIALLY YOU, FARLEY.

THE ONLY AMERICAN TO JOIN ME OF HIS OWN FREE WILL. MY LOYAL SUBJECT...
...WHO SAW HIMSELF A KING IN MY KINGDOM.
DID I SAY KING? PERHAPS THAT WASN'T THE BEST--
URK!
SNAP
NO.
IT WASN'T.
I FOLLOWED THE TRUCK TO HERE, RIGHT WHERE MISS LANE SHOT AT YOU...I CHECKED-- BURBANK SEZ THIS HOTEL MONOLITH WAS FINISHED NEARLY TEN YEARS AGO, BUT NEVER OPENED.
GOONS CAME OUTTA NOWHERE AN' STARTED UNLOADIN' WHEN I SCRAMMED BACK TO YOU.
WHEN WAS THE BUILDING DEMOLISHED?
EVERYONE SEEMS TO KNOW IT WAS GUTTED, BUT NOBODYS SURE JUST WHEN.

OR IF..
MARGO, YOU SHOT AT ME FROM JUST OVER THERE...
THE BULLET PASSED OVER MY SHOULDER AND--
...SHATTERED THAT WINDOW.
IT'S UNLIKELY TO HAVE BEEN RE-PLACED, AND THERE'S NO BROKEN GLASS ON THE GROUND.
SOMETHING UNUSUAL IS AT WORK HERE.
I BELIEVE KHAN AND HIS MENTAL POWERS ARE BEHIND IT.
IF I CAN FOCUS ENOUGH OF MY CONCENTRATION...
OH!
AMAZING!
I-I CAN SCARCELY BELIEVE HE DID THIS!
DID WHAT? WHAT ARE YOU SEEING?
25¢
5¢
LUXOR
CAB

HIWAN KHAN IS SING HIS CON-IDERABLE MENTAL BILITY TO MASK S INTENT FROM THE ENTIRE CITY.
WHAT CAN YOU DO ALONE?

WE HAD THE SAME TEACHER. I CAN SEE THROUGH HIS ILLUSIONS, FIND THE CENTER OF HIS POWER AND TURN IT AGAINST HIM.

I MAY NEED YOUR HELP.
YOUR FATHER AND HIS DEVICE ARE OBVIOUSLY THE KEY, BUT AS YET I CANNOT SEE THE LOCK...
WAIT HERE.

...BUT COME QUICKLY WHEN I CALL!

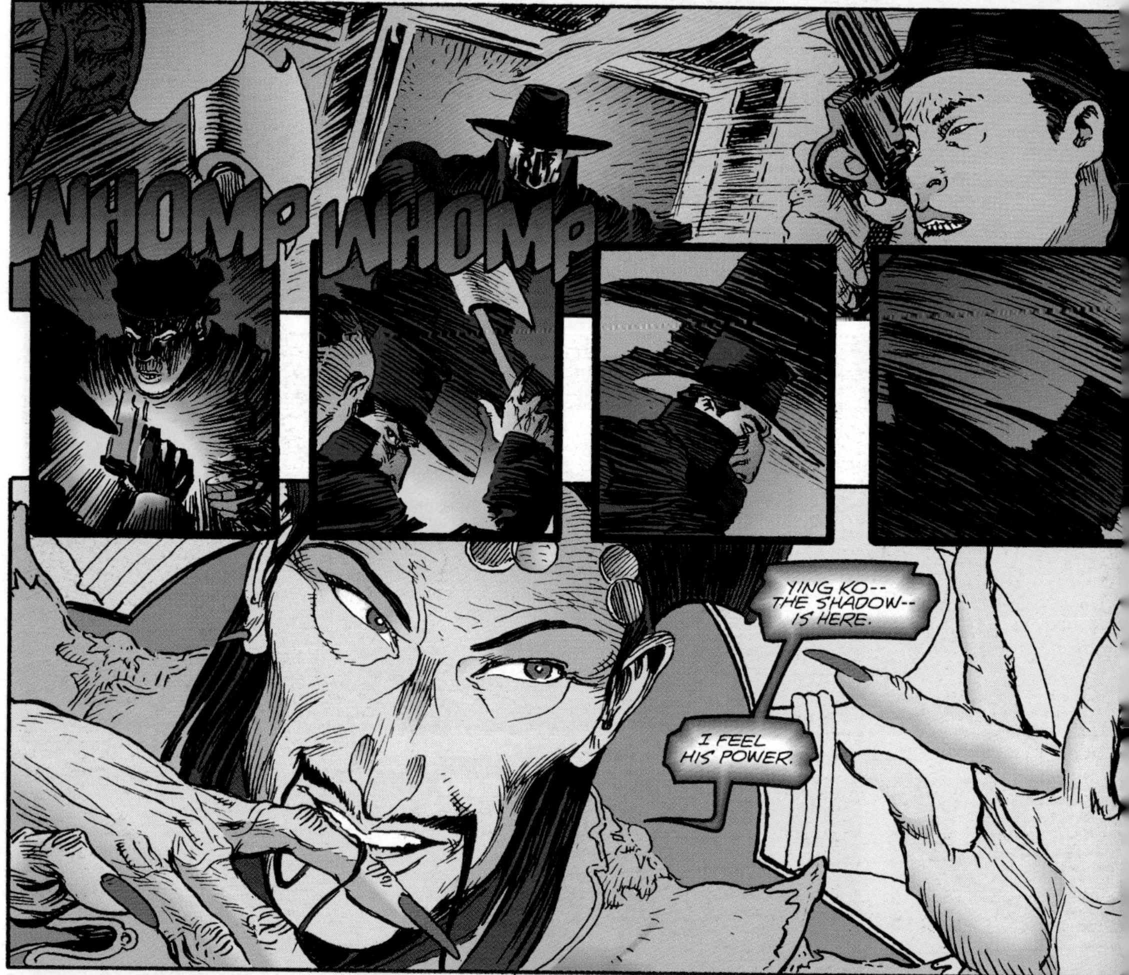
WHOMP WHOMP
YING KO-- THE SHADOW-- IS HERE.
I FEEL HIS POWER.

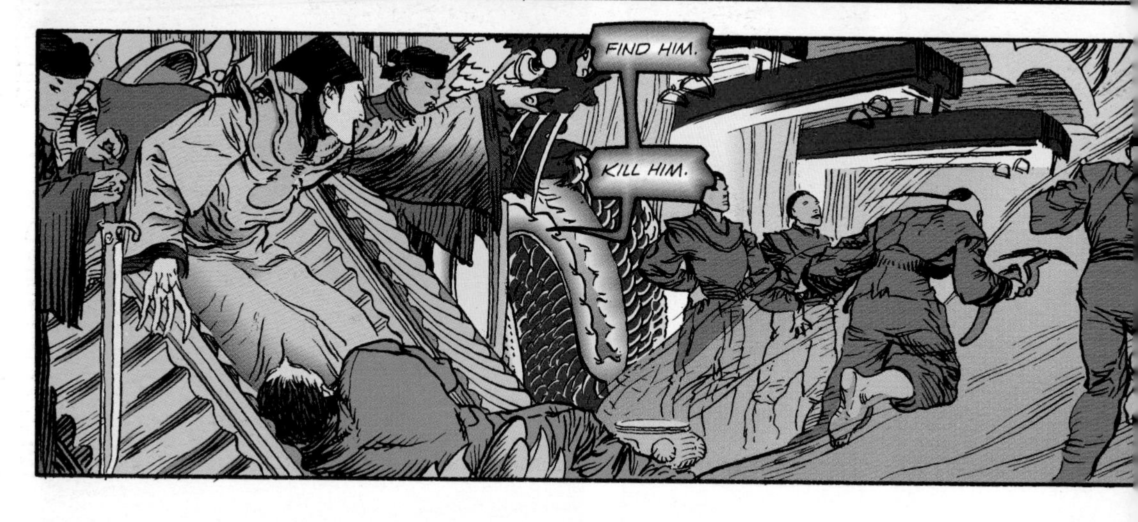
FIND HIM.
KILL HIM.

BLAM! BLAMM! BLAM!
HA
HAHA
HAHAHAHAHAHAHA

BLAM!
BLAM!
BLAM!
BLAM!
BLAM!
BALAMM!
BLAM!
BLAM!
NOW I SEND YOU MASTER TULKU'S PURHBA, YING KO...
I WILL SEE IF YOU HAVE THE STRENGTH TO FIGHT THE BLADE, MY ASSASSINS...
...AND ME!

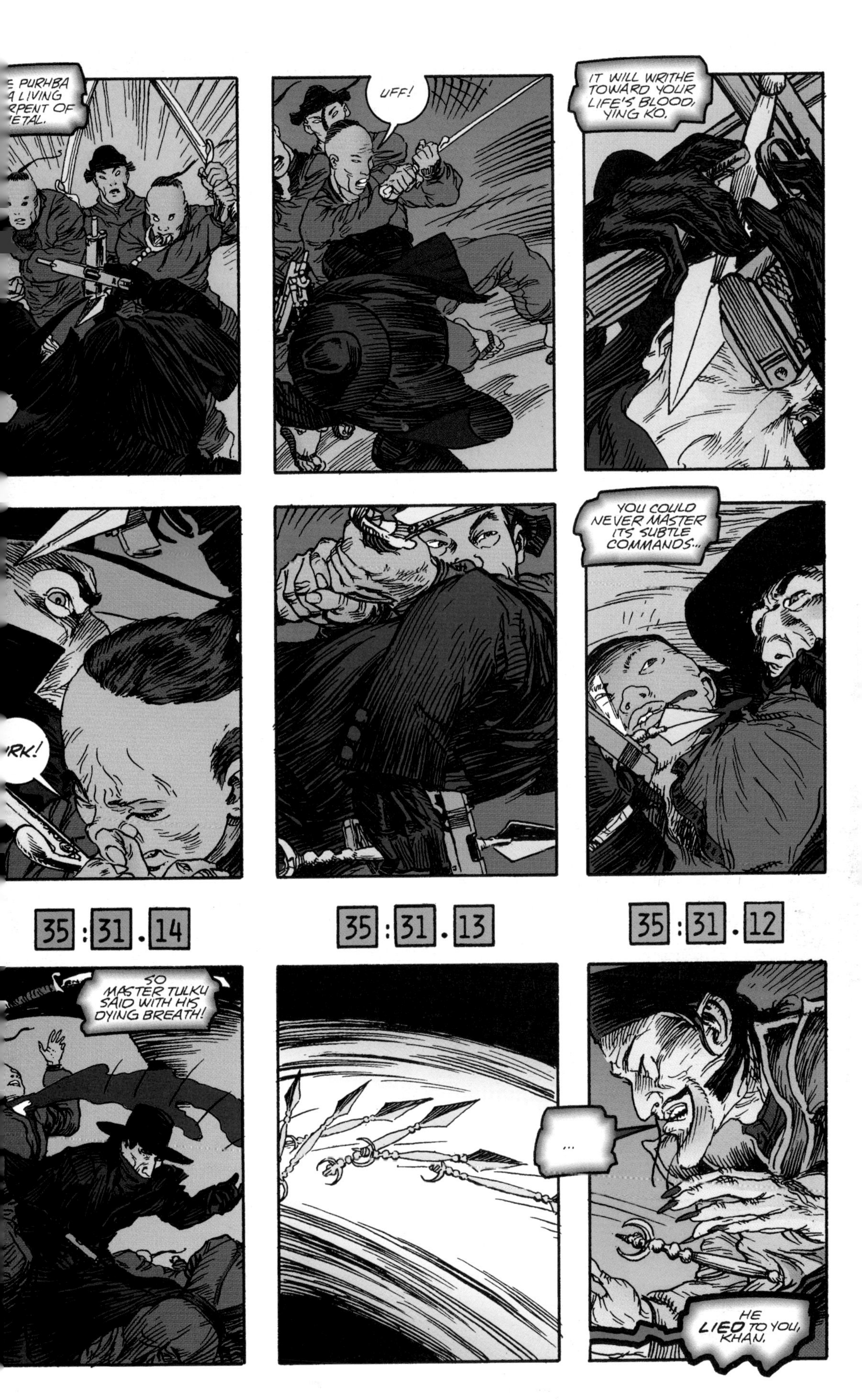
E PURHBA
A LIVING
RPENT OF
ETAL.
UFF!
IT WILL WRITHE TOWARD YOUR LIFE'S BLOOD, YING KO.
RK!
YOU COULD NEVER MASTER ITS SUBTLE COMMANDS...
35:31.14
35:31.13
35:31.12
SO MASTER TULKU SAID WITH HIS DYING BREATH!
...
HE **LIED** TO YOU, KHAN.

SHREVVY!
THAT'S WHAT HE SAW!
LOOKS LIKE A SIGNAL TO ME. C'MON.
DAD!
MARGO? WHAT'S GOING ON?
WHERE AM I?
"IT'S NOT IMPORTANT, DAD. WHERE IS FARLEY CLAYMORE... AND HIS SPHERE?"

YING KO.

BLAMM!
KRAKK

HAAIIEEE!

5 : 21 . 19
HERE'S FARLEY'S SPHERE, BUT I HAVEN'T SEEN HIM FOR DAYS!
THIS WORK 'T CLAYMORE'S... WONDER WHO DID IT?!
YOU DID IT, DAD. NOW DISARM IT!
IMPRESSIVE WORK. I WONDER WHAT THESE METAL DISCS ARE?
BZZT!
OOPS.
DAD!
FOLLOWING ME DOWN HERE HAS LED YOU AWAY FROM THE BOMB--

I WISH I REMEMBERED DOING THIS!
THE TIMER!
LET'S SEE...
OH, DEAR.
00:14.3
DAD!
BLAM! BLAM!
THAT BOMB IS COUNTING DOWN YOUR TIME ON EARTH, SHIWAN KHAN.
I WILL DISPOSE OF YOU, THEN THE BOMB.
YOU WILL DIE FIRST.
THE TIMER IS BOOBY-TRAPPED-- THE BOMB CANNOT BE DEFUSED.
FACE THE FACT, YING KO-- YOU ARE BEATEN.
EVEN IF YOU KILL ME NOW, THE BOMB WILL GO OFF--YOU AND EVERYTHING FOR MILES AROUND WILL BE BLASTED INTO SLAG...

MARGO!
SHE CAN DO NOTHING.
YOUR FATHER MUST NOT DEFUSE THE BOMB--REMOVE HIS IMPLOSION DEVICE FROM THE BERYLLIUM SPHERE--
SEAL IT IN THE ILVER COFFIN AND GET OUT!
DAD, WAIT! THIS WAY!
SHUT THE LID AND RUN FOR IT!
00 : 03 . 49
00 : 02 . 36
00 : 01 . 14
00 : 00 . 59
00 : 00 . 05
00 : 00 . 00
00 : 00 . 00
00 : 00 . 00
STOP!
YOU SHOULD NEVER HAVE TOLD ME THE SARCOPHAGUS WAS THE SOURCE OF YOUR STRENGTH, SHIWAN KHAN.

KAW
WHUMPF
WELL, THAT WAS PRECISELY MY CALCULATED EFFECT! THE IMPLOSIVE--
NOT NOW, DAD.
SHREVVY ...?
THE BOSS IS TOUGH, BUT JEEZE... I DUNNO...
I'M ALL RIGHT, SHREVVY...
LAMONT.

BUT ONLY JUST. KHAN'S ACUITY OF MIND WAS STRONGER THAN MY OWN. UNHARMED, HE WOULD HAVE TRIUMPHED.
IN THE END, IT WAS MASTER TULKU'S PURHBA AND ITS IMPAIRING WOUND THAT SAVED A WORLD.

THE PATIENT IS RECOVERING NICELY, DOCTOR TAM. WILL YOU BE TAKING HIM BACK WITH YOU?

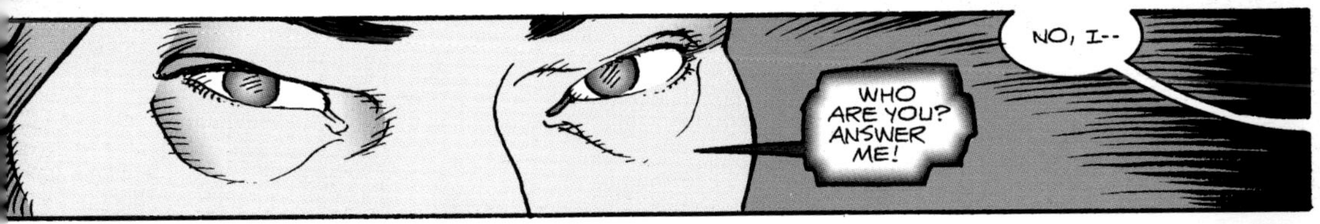
NO, I--
WHO ARE YOU? ANSWER ME!

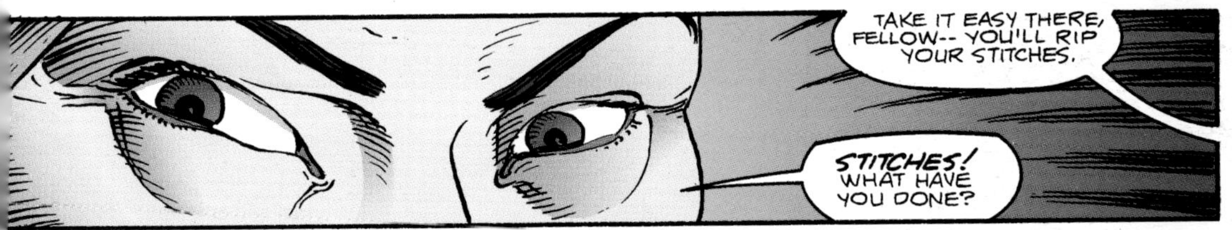
TAKE IT EASY THERE, FELLOW-- YOU'LL RIP YOUR STITCHES.
STITCHES! WHAT HAVE YOU DONE?

Y SAVED UR LIFE, HAT'S ALL.
WE ST HAD REMOVE LITTLE YOUR ONTAL OBE.

DON'T WORRY, YOU WON'T MISS IT. IT'S A SMALL PART THAT NOBODY EVER USES...

...UNLESS, OF COURSE, YOU BELIEVE IN TELEPATHY.
WAIT! COME BACK!

I AM THE HEIR TO GENGHIS KHAN!!
AND THAT'S YOUR TRUE STORY?
WELL, I EMBELLISHED IT A LITTLE. YOU KNOW, TO MAKE IT MORE DRAMATIC.
AND YOU SAY THIS WAS LAMONT CRANSTON?
NEW YORK'S OWN MAN-ABOUT-TOWN HIMSELF.
MARGO LANE-- SHE'LL BACK YOUR STORY UP?
WELL, SHE HAS A VESTED INTEREST IN KEEPING THIS SECRET. HER REPUTATION AND HER FATHER'S WORK...
IN OTHER WORDS: NO, SHE WON'T BACK YOU UP.
WELL, I'LL LOOK INTO IT AND SEE IF I CAN DO ANYTHING, OKAY?
THESE PAPERS... THESE ARE YOUR NOTES?
YEP, EVERYTHING I HAVE.
I'LL NEED 'EM.

GREAT. I KNEW I COULD COUNT ON YOU.
HE CAN COUNT ON ME, ALL RIGHT.
THE END

"The official, full-colour movie adaptation of Mike Richardson's *The Mask* is also available from Boxtree. The following section contains the uncoloured final edit of *The Mask*'s first 12 pages."

THE TENTH CENTURY A.D.
AT WILL E THE LACE!
BE QUICK, WITCH. WE'VE TRAVELED TO THE END OF THE WORLD FOR THIS, BUT I FEAR WE HAVEN'T GONE FAR ENOUGH.
OH LOKI, ANCIENT ONE. THY MISCHIEF MUST DWELL NOW IN WATERS, BASE AND BLAND. IN WAVES AND SAND THY MAGIC WILL FOR-EVER SLEEP.
BACK TO THE SHIP, MEN-- **HURRY!** THIS LAND IS NOW **CURSED**, AND WE MUST NEVER SET FOOT HERE AGAIN.

EDGE CITY-- PRESENT DAY.
A SHORT DISTANCE OFFSHORE...
KER-CHA
KARACK

WHERE'D THIS COME FROM? IT'S SUPPOSED TO BE HOT AND SUNNY.
EXCUSE ME, CHARLIE, BUT CAN WE GO OVER THESE STATS? THE REPORT IS WAY OVER-DUE, AND...
STANLEY, PLEASE, I WAS UP ALL NIGHT WATCHING THE COUPLE IN THE NEXT BUILDING, AND I'M EXHAUSTED.
BE A PAL-AND-A-HALF AND HANDLE THIS ONE FOR ME? I'LL OWE YOU A LARGE ONE. THANKS.
THERE'S A NOTE IN MY DRAWER THAT YOU NEEDED TO SEE ME.
OH, YES! I DID... I MEAN, I DO.
I GOT THOSE TICKETS YOU WANTED. I THOUGHT WE'D EAT FIRST, AND THEN...
OH, STANLEY, THIS IS GREAT. YOU ARE SO NICE. YOU EALLY ARE. CHARLIE, ISN'T STANLEY THE NICEST GUY?
MY BEST GIRLFRIEND IS IN TOWN, AND SHE'S JUST DYING TO GO TO THIS.
BUT... BUT...

THAT WAS THE MOST SICKENING DISPLAY I'VE EVER WITNESSED. I'M NAUSEOUS. I'M ACTUALLY NAUSEOUS.
WHAT WAS I SUPPOSED TO DO?
ANYTHING YOU WANTED-- FOR THOSE TICKETS.
YOU SPEND TOO MUCH TIME BEING NICE TO GIRLS. WHAT YOU NEED IS A LITTLE CHANGE OF PACE, BUDDY.
TELL YOU WHAT. TONIGHT I'M GOING TO LET YOU OBSERVE THE OLD MASTER IN ACTION, AT THE HOTTEST NEW JOINT IN TOWN-- THE COCO BONGO CLUB.
CAN YOU REALLY GET US IN?
ARE YOU KIDDING? JUST LEAVE EVERYTHING TO ME. THIS IS GOING TO BE THE PERFECT NIGHT ON THE TOWN.
I DON'T BELIEVE IT. WILL YOU TAKE A LOOK AT THAT!

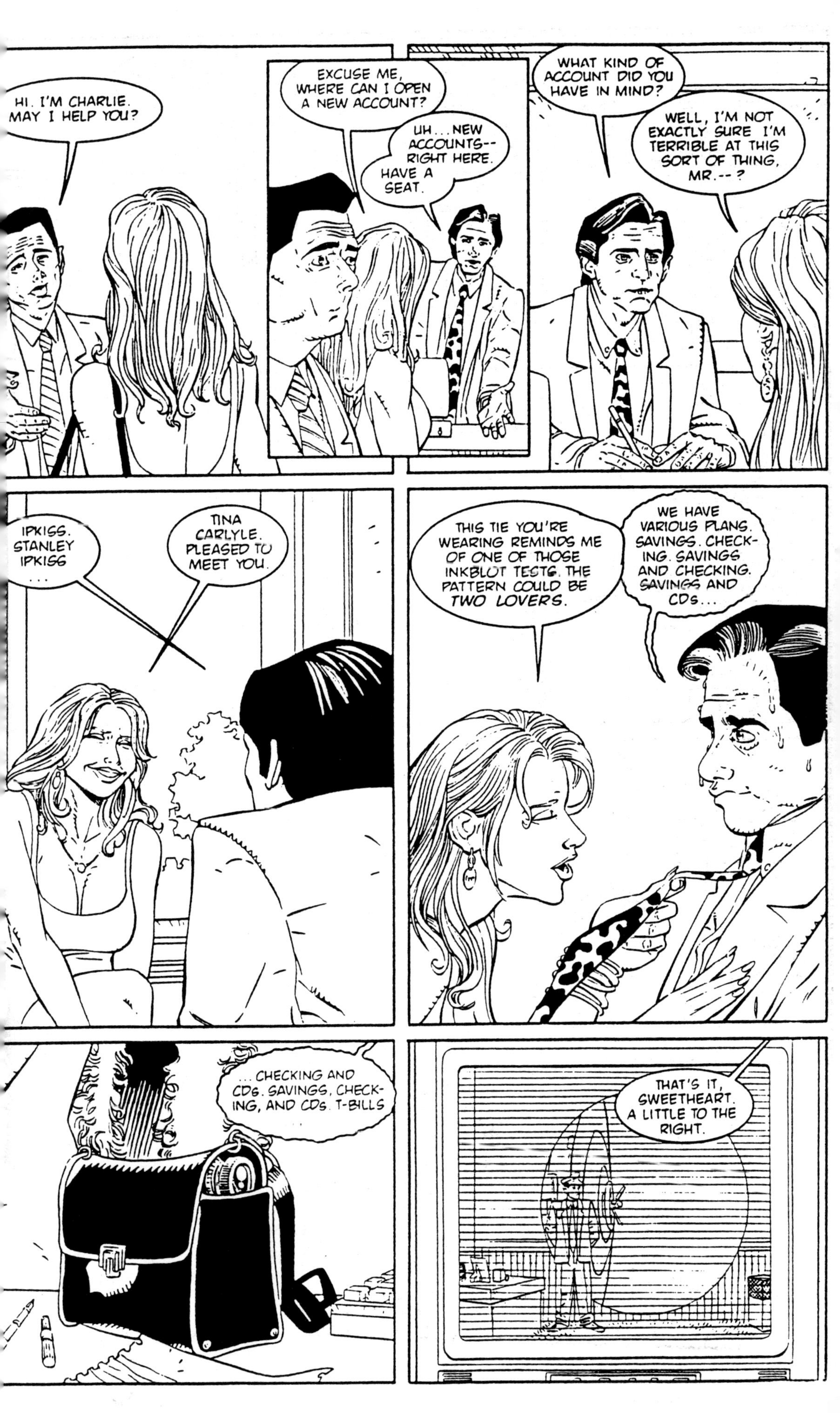
HI. I'M CHARLIE. MAY I HELP YOU?
EXCUSE ME, WHERE CAN I OPEN A NEW ACCOUNT?
UH... NEW ACCOUNTS-- RIGHT HERE. HAVE A SEAT.
WHAT KIND OF ACCOUNT DID YOU HAVE IN MIND?
WELL, I'M NOT EXACTLY SURE I'M TERRIBLE AT THIS SORT OF THING, MR.-- ?
IPKISS. STANLEY IPKISS ...
TINA CARLYLE. PLEASED TO MEET YOU.
THIS TIE YOU'RE WEARING REMINDS ME OF ONE OF THOSE INKBLOT TESTS. THE PATTERN COULD BE TWO LOVERS.
WE HAVE VARIOUS PLANS. SAVINGS. CHECKING. SAVINGS AND CHECKING. SAVINGS AND CDs...
...CHECKING AND CDs. SAVINGS, CHECKING, AND CDs. T-BILLS
THAT'S IT, SWEETHEART. A LITTLE TO THE RIGHT.

WHAT DO YOU THINK, DOCTOR?
LAYOUT'S NOT BAD. WE GOT US A SWEET LITTLE PERKINS / JENNING TIME LOCK.
SO CAN YOU PULL IT OFF?
SURE. THIS IS *THE DOCTOR* YOU'RE TALKIN' TO, BUT I GOT ONE QUESTION... WHAT ABOUT *THE SWEDE*?

EVERYTHING IS THE SWEDE'S GRIFT. HE OWNS YOU. HE OWNS THE CLUB. HE OWNS THIS WHOLE STINKIN' TOWN.

THINGS CHANGE.

BUT WE'RE GONNA NEED SOME CASH. SO... FIRST WE TAKE THE BANK. *THEN* WE TAKE THE SWEDE.
THEN, MY FRIENDS, SCHOOL IS OUT.

AND THIS CITY IS OUR PLAYGROUND.

ATER, AT RIPLEY'S AUTO GARAGE...
HELLO?
NG
CLANK
CRASH
BAM
HANG ON. HANG ON. DON'T GET YOUR PANTIES IN A TWIST.
HEY, BURT, WHAT THE HECK IS THIS?
OHH... I DUNNO. ABOUT SEVEN HUN-DRED BUCKS.
NOW, WHAT CAN I DO FOR YOU, BUB?
I'M HERE FOR THE GREEN CIVIC. I BROUGHT IT IN FOR AN OIL CHANGE.
YOU ... CIVIC?
YOUR BRAKE DRUMS ARE SHOT. THEY NEED TO BE REPLACED IMMEDIATELY. AND YOU'LL NEED A NEW TRANSMISSION AND MUFFLER WHILE WE'RE AT IT.
YOU'RE LUCKY WE CAUGHT THESE OTHER THINGS BEFORE THEY CAUSED SOME SERIOUS TROUBLE.
OF COURSE, IT'S UP TO YOU. YOU FIX IT-- OR GET BURNED IN IT.
UM... WELL, FIX IT, OF COURSE... I GUESS. BUT CAN YOU PROVIDE ME WITH... UM... A LOANER?
SURE, SURE. NO PROBLEM. Heh Heh. AND ONLY NINE-TEEN BUCKS A DAY.

THE COCO BONGO CLUB.
Coco Bongo
IT'S A CLASSIC. USED TO BELONG TO ELVIS.
HEY, STANLEY. C'MON, YOU'RE LATE.
HOW MUCH CASH ARE YOU CARRYING?
I DUNNO-- FIFTY OR SIXTY BUCKS.
GIMME.
NO WAY.
HEY, I'LL PAY YOU BACK. C'MON, MAN, YOU WANT TO STAND OUT HERE ALL NIGHT?
THAT'S BETTER. FOLLOW ME.

BY!
CHARLIE, HOW YOU DOIN', MAN? LONG TIME NO SEE.
HAVE A GOOD TIME, CHARLIE.
HEY, WAIT A MINUTE, CHARLIE.
EVER-
CH-THE-
ROPE.
HEY! I'M A BLEEDER!
HUH...?
OH... MR. IPKISS. HI.

ARE YOU OKAY?
KAPOW
IT'S JUST A LOANER. MY CAR'S IN THE SHOP BEING PREPARED FOR... UH... THE BIG RACE. YEAH, THAT'S IT.
RACE?
YEAH... UH... THE, UM... TALLAHASSEE THREE THOUSAND. I'VE WON IT... er... FOUR YEARS IN A ROW... CONSECUTIVELY.

WELL, GOOD NIGHT. GOOD LUCK IN THE RACE.
TAHOOCHIE
COUGH
sputter
THE TALLAHASSEE... RIIIGHT.
RATTLE

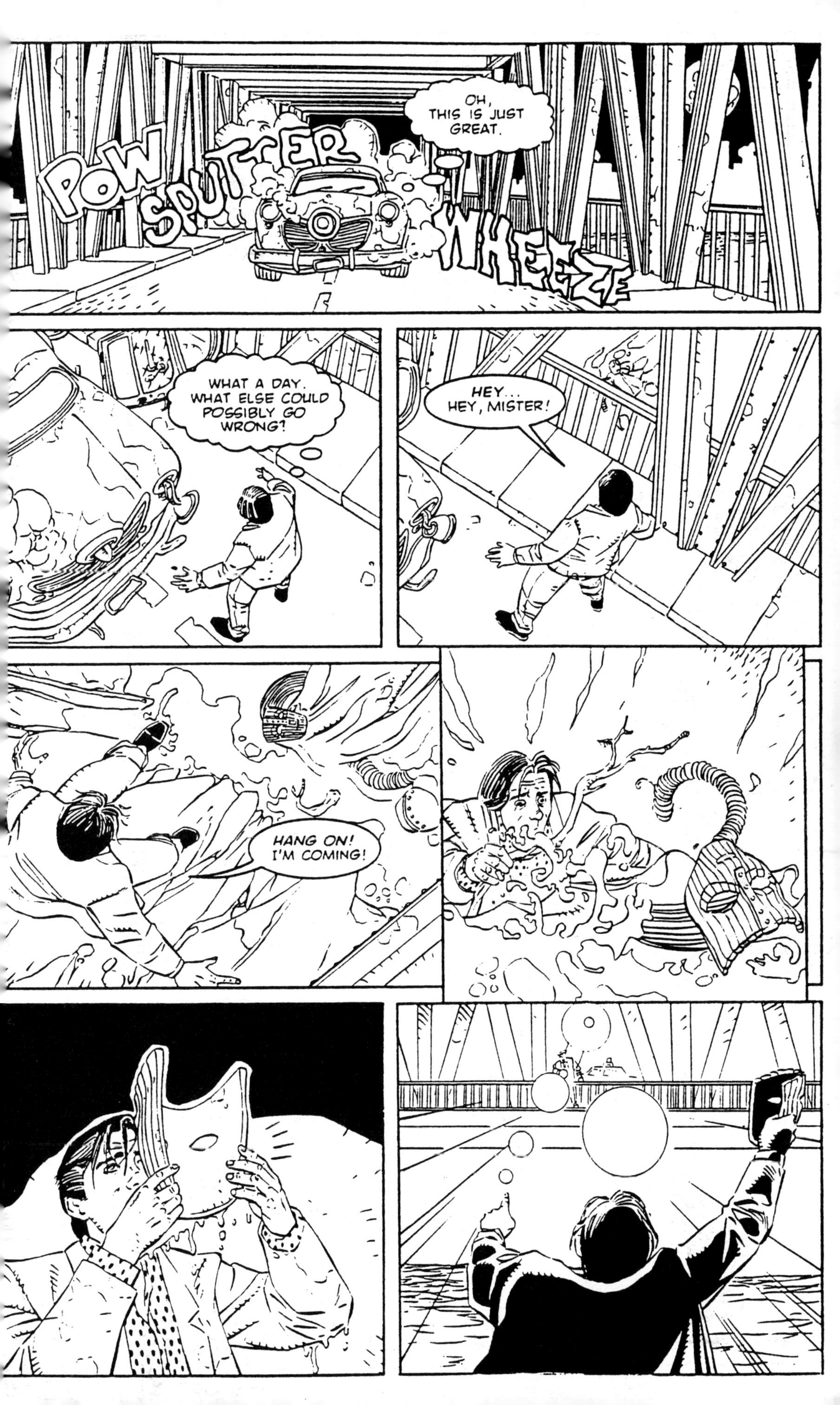
POW
SPUTTER
WHEEZE
OH, THIS IS JUST GREAT.
WHAT A DAY. WHAT ELSE COULD POSSIBLY GO WRONG?
HEY... HEY, MISTER!
HANG ON! I'M COMING!

THANKS, RENO-- YOU'RE THE GREATEST.
G'NIGHT, DOLL.
NICE PERFORMANCE, BABY, BUT NOT AS NICE AS THE CAMERA TRICK YOU PULLED OFF AT THE BANK.
YEAH, WELL, DON'T GET USED TO IT. I'M THROUGH WITH YOUR CONS. I'M A SINGER NOW--AND THAT'S IT.
SO YOU'RE A SINGER, HUH? AND YOU HAD SUCH A TERRIFIC CAREER BEFORE YOU LATCHED ON TO ME.
DON'T PUSH ME. I MIGHT JUST TAKE A WALK--ONE I SHOULD HAVE TAKEN A LONG TIME AGO.
HEY, C'MERE. YOU TAKE A HIKE AND WHO'S GONNA KISS YOU LIKE DORIAN?
THAT'S RIGHT, BABY. C'MERE.
NOBODY.
SORRY. I NEVER GET PERSONAL IN FRONT OF THE HELP.
SHE KILLS ME.
SHE JUST MIGHT, MAN. SHE JUST MIGHT.